GRAND JOY

Written by Kim C. Lee and K. Denise Hendershot
Illustrated by Gabrielle Fludd

GRAND JOY by Kim C. Lee and K. Denise Hendershot
Published by Kim C. Lee

Copyright © 2021 Kim C. Lee

ISBN: 978-1-7361273-6-0

Visit the authors online at www.kimcleewrites.com and www.diverseluv.com.

For anyone struggling to find a reason to celebrate life,
start with the smallest things as they bring the grandest joy. *- K.C.L*

For my Grand Joys, you light up my life and will forever
give me a reason to smile. *- K.D.H*

What is GRAND JOY ?

There are so many people, places, and things
where we find **GRAND JOY** to make our hearts sing.
The happiness in life, the moments you share,
the joy that you get and give everywhere!

GRAND JOY is baking cookies with Mom wearing our special homemade aprons. Wooden spoons and measuring cups, the sweet taste of chocolate chips!

GRAND JOY is splashing in puddles
while wearing rain boots and chasing friends.
The warm feeling of sunshine on our faces
as we watch the fluffy clouds float by.

GRAND JOY is blowing big soapy bubbles
and sudsy spheres wandering in the air.
Jumping and running, clapping and poking –
"Quick, don't let them hit the ground!"

GRAND JOY is riding your bike,
the wind at your back, and tooting your horn!
It's opening day at the swimming pool –
"Who will be the first to make a splash?"

LAUGHING, CHUCKLING, CHORTLING, HOWLING!

HOOTING, HOLLERING, SNICKERING, SMILING!

So many things
that bring us delight!

This joy,

GRAND
JOY,

has so much might!

GRAND JOY is beach time with family
and getting knocked down by big ocean waves.
Sandcastles, seashells, buckets, and shovels!
Burying our toes in the soft golden sand.

GRAND JOY is the smell of homemade biscuits, melted butter, and lots of honey. Fluffy, light, and flaky goodness – *"Pass them along - I'll take two!"*

GRAND JOY is twirling in the curtains,
all wrapped up in the waving of soft silk fabric.
Dizzy, spinning, peeking, and smiling!
"I'm hiding, I'm hiding - can you see me?"

GRAND JOY is Dad tickling away my fears,
rolling around and kicking in laughter.
Trying to get away to catch my breath,
"Wait! Don't stop - let's laugh some more!"

CHEERFUL, EXCITED, MERRY, GLAD!

REJOICING, AMUSED, JOLLY, RAD!

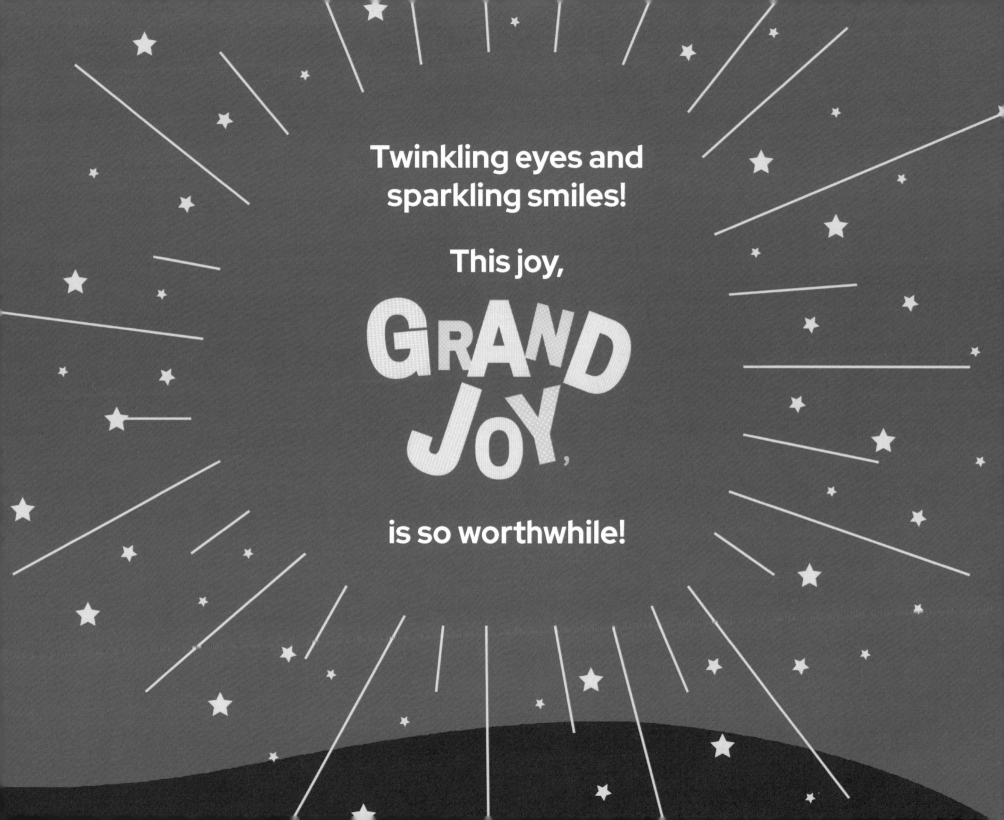

Twinkling eyes and
sparkling smiles!

This joy,

GRAND
JOY,

is so worthwhile!

Of all the things that bring us joy,
our grandparents' visits are tops!
Excited to know they're headed our way –
"Are they here yet? We just can't wait!"

High-fives and smiles meet us at the door,
and Gram always smells like vanilla.
She lifts us high in the air,
and laughter rolls from our bellies!

Grandpa reads our favorite books
while his glasses slide down his nose.
Funny, kind, and scary voices!
"I'm listening! What will happen next?"

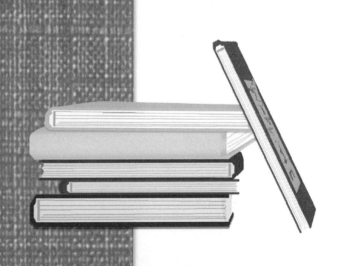

Music echoes all through the house
while Grandpa and Gram dance in the kitchen.
We all help to make our favorite dish –
"Spaghetti! Spaghetti! Spaghetti!"

HAPPY,
CHIPPER,
BUBBLY,
LIVELY,!

VIBRANT, HEARTY, FUNNY, SPRIGHTLY!

A feeling of warmth,
enjoyment, and glee!

A grandparent's love is

GRAND JOY,

for me!

There are so many people, places, and things
where we find GRAND JOY to make our hearts sing.
The happiness in life, the moments you share,
the joy that you get and give everywhere!

I am GRAND JOY.

You are GRAND JOY.

We are all GRAND JOY !

K. Denise Hendershot

Kim C. Lee

DENISE K. HENDERSHOT and **KIM C. LEE** met over ten years ago and have been friends since then. They are both passionate about their families, personal growth, and helping others learn and understand the gifts they bring to the world. In 2020, the global pandemic brought them closer together and after a multitude of conversations focused on how important it is to appreciate all things in life regardless of how big or small, *Grand Joy* was written.

DENISE K. HENDERSHOT is a veteran and diversity, inclusion, and equity advocate from Virginia who focuses on educating middle and high school students on the importance and benefits of diversity and inclusion. She loves writing and blogging about any topic that sparks engagement and diverse dialogues. Her writing credits include a contribution to the *Whose Shoes Are You Wearing?* journal. Denise also has a podcast, *Truth and Coffee Time*, that she co-hosts with her husband of 30+ years. You can find Denise online at www.diverseluv.com.

KIM C. LEE is a technology professional, children's book author, and literacy advocate from Maryland. Her written works include *The Night Owl* and *Meet Frankie Jordan*. Kim is motivated to use books to highlight the experiences and perspectives of African American children. When she is not writing, Kim enjoys spending time with family and providing content creation support to other individuals pursuing their authoring dreams. She is also a member of the Society of Children's Book Writers and Illustrators (SCBWI) and the Maryland Writers' Association. You can find Kim online at www.kimcleewrites.com.